SCHUMANN

Drei Fantasiestücke

OP.111

Edited & annotated by

HOWARD FERGUSON

THE ASSOCIATED BOARD OF
THE ROYAL SCHOOLS OF MUSIC

CONTENTS

Sehr rasch, mit leidenschaflichem Vortrag

1   *page* 6

Ziemlich langsam

2   10

Kräftig und sehr markiert

3   13

INTRODUCTION

Robert Schumann (1810–1856)

SOURCES

A Autographs: 1) Sketch of No.2; No.3 complete (Chicago, Newberry Library).
2) Start of No.2 (Leningrad, Bibliothek Saltykow-Stschedrin).
3) Complete autograph fair-copy (Zwickau, Robert-Schumann-Haus, MS Nr.10307).

B 1st edition: *Drei Fantasiestücke*, Op.111; C.F.Peters, Leipzig [1852], Pl.No.3525.

The present edition follows B.

THE WORK

Like *Waldscenen*, Op.82, but unlike the majority of Schumann's best known piano works, the *Drei Fantasiestücke* were written towards the end of his life. The *Attacca* marked at the end of Nos.1 & 2 (unusual in Schumann) shows that the three pieces were intended to form a single work.

PEDALLING

In piano works from Op.5 onwards Schumann often indicated the use of the sustaining pedal by no more than the word *Pedal* at the beginning of a movement. Its precise interpretation was left to the initiative and musicality of the player, the additional marks *Ped.* ✳ being provided only when some special effect was required. In this connection it is helpful to remember two points: 1) the presence of rests and/or staccatos does not necessarily preclude the use of pedal; and 2) it is always needed to sustain the low note(s) of a chord or arpeggio that cannot be stretched by the hand.

Though the *una corda* or 'soft pedal' is not indicated in the *Drei Fantasiestücke* - elsewhere Schumann generally employed the word *Verschiebung* - it can of course be used at the player's discretion, provided that does not mean at every appearance of a *p*.

TEMPO

As a rule Schumann used German tempo indications, supplementing them with metronome marks. In the present edition the more familiar Italian equivalents of the former have been added within square brackets by the editor. One would have thought that the metronome marks would solve all questions of tempo, but unfortunately they do not. For Schumann's marks so often seem at variance with what appears to be the intended mood of the piece concerned that it is always wise to treat them with extreme caution. One's suspicions concerning their reliability are strengthened by the fact that many of them (though not, as it happens, those in the *Drei Fantasiestücke*) were altered, sometimes very considerably, in the posthumous Instructive Edition edited by his widow, Clara. (It is noteworthy, too, that Saint-Saëns wrote to the conductor Paul Taffanel in 1902: 'It was Mme Schumann herself who told me that there was no need to take any account of her husband's

metronome markings.') The sort of differences that occur can be seen by comparing the original metronome marks with Clara's revisions for the thirteen pieces in *Kinderscenen*, Op.15, as tabulated in the Introduction to the Associated Board edition of 1981. These show that Clara's marks are generally slower than Robert's, but occasionally faster. Had his been consistently either too slow or too fast one could have assumed that the machine he used was incorrectly adjusted. But since this is not so, and since Clara's marks invariably seem the more musical, it is hard to avoid the conclusion that Schumann often failed to check his metronome marks against actual performance.[1]

In the present edition, Robert's metronome mark is given at the beginning of each piece, and the editor's suggested tempo at the end. It should be understood, however, that the editorial markings are neither authoritative nor binding.

Note that Schumann often omitted the necessary *a tempo* following a *rit*. In such cases it is implied from the beginning of either the following bar or the following phrase.

ORNAMENTATION

The only ornaments in the *Drei Fantasiestücke* are single small notes and inverted mordents.

Single small note: ♪, ♪. The first is short and anticipates the beat. The second, which only occurs in No.2, bb.13 & 62, seems here to require a long appoggiatura; though elsewhere it, too, is often short.

Inverted mordent: 𝅘𝅥 = ♫ (only in No.2, bb.14 & 63).

RHYTHMIC CONVENTIONS

In No.1, b.21, and the central section of No.2, Schumann almost certainly expected the player to follow the old convention of adjusting duple rhythms to coincide with triple when the two occur simultaneously, as here shown in small notes above or below the stave. (In the source it is actually printed thus in No.2, bb.14, 34 & 63; though, oddly enough, not in bb.37–40.) Note, however, that the final r.h. semiquaver in No.1, b.18, was probably meant to be short, as written, for it has the character of an anticipatory grace-note. In No.2, b.32, it is uncertain whether the final r.h. quaver should be played as written, or as a triplet-quaver coinciding with the $\frac{B}{G}$.

[1]The problem is interestingly discussed in Brian Schlotel's essay 'Schumann and the Metronome' (*Robert Schumann: the man and his music*, ed. Alan Walker; Barrie and Jenkins, London 1972, pp.109–119), though his conclusions are somewhat inconsistent. He begins by upholding Robert's marks against Clara's revisions. He then admits that the finale of the 2nd Symphony taken at Schumann's 'breathtaking speed of ♩ = 170 would certainly ruin the Symphony's effect even if the players *could* take the semiquaver swirls at that pace'; and ♩ = 84 at the beginning of the Piano Concerto 'seems impossibly fast' for the first pages. Yet he ends by saying that 'Schumann's metronome marks do, despite all, give a useful guide to how he wanted his music played'. All of which sounds rather like having your cake and eating it.

THIS EDITION

In the present edition numbered footnotes are concerned with textual matters, and lettered footnotes with interpretation. Redundant accidentals have been omitted. Editorial accidentals, notes, rests, dynamics, etc., are printed either in small type or within square brackets, and editorial slurs, ties, and 'hairpin' *cresc.* and *dim.* signs are crossed with a small vertical line. Curved brackets indicate that a note should not be struck. Schumann's few fingerings are shown in italics: the rest are editorial. The editor has at times altered the original distribution of notes on the two staves, when doing so might make them easier to read. Generally his aim has been to place r.h. notes on the upper stave and l.h. notes on the lower; but occasionally it has been more convenient to use the signs ⌊ and ⌈ to indicate the r.h. and l.h. respectively.

Warmest thanks are due to The British Library Board for providing access to the 1st edition of the work, and for giving permission for it to be used in establishing the present text.

HOWARD FERGUSON
Cambridge 1987

DREI FANTASIESTÜCKE
THREE FANTASY PIECES
Op.111

Sehr rasch, mit leidenschaftlichem Vortrag M.M. ♩ = 84
[Molto vivace ed appassionatamente]

SCHUMANN
1851

(a) Gracenotes before the beat.

AB 1988

(b) See the Introduction, under Rhythmic Conventions.

Ziemlich langsam M.M. ♩ = 72
[Piuttosto lento]

Etwas bewegter
[Poco più mosso]

For small hands:

Erstes Tempo
[Tempo primo]

(e) See the Introduction, under Rhythmic Conventions.

Attacca Nr. 3

Ed: ♩ = c.63,   b.26 ♩ = c.96

Kräftig und sehr markiert M.M. ♩ = 96
[Con forza, assai marcato]

3

f

Mit. Ped.

(a) For small hands:

Ed: ♩ = c.92

6/89

1) B.50, r.h. lower chord 2: the G is missing in the source; but see b.16.

AB 1988

Processed and printed by
Halstan & Co. Ltd., Amersham, Bucks., England